The Reef Riders

by Corinne Fenton

Illustrated by Mark Wilson

Chill Out is published by Nelson Thomson Learning and is distributed as follows:

AUSTRALIA
Thomson Learning
102 Dodds Street
Southbank 3006
Victoria

NEW ZEALAND
Nelson Price Milburn
1 Te Puni Street
Petone
Wellington

First published in 2002
10 9 8 7 6 5 4 3 2 1
05 04 03 02

The Reef Raiders
ISBN 0 17 010 512 1

Project commissioned and managed by Lorraine Bambrough-Kelly,
The Writer's Style
Designed by Leigh Ashforth @ watershed art & design
Series design by James Lowe
Illustrations by Mark Wilson
Printed in China by Midas Printing (Asia) Ltd

Acknowledgements
Thank you to the teachers and students of St John's Primary School, Heidelberg;
St Francis Xavier Primary School, Montmorency; Luther College, Wonga Park;
and the Atchison and Burns families. Thanks also to Lynn Howie and the Stage 3
boys at Alstonville Primary School for their assistance in developing this series.

Nelson Thomson Australia Pty Limited ACN 058 280 149 (incorporated in Victoria)
trading as Nelson Thomson Learning.

Contents

Chapter 1

On Eastern Beach

The light was so bright. I shaded my eyes from its glare.

Then the blinding light vanished. And a heavy sea mist began to close in around me.

It was mid-term vacation. My mum had rented an old house at Eastern Beach.

From the front window of the house we could see the surf. And the golden sand.

I couldn't wait to get down there.

I threw my backpack on the bed.

'Come on fella,' I called to Buster. 'Let's go for a run along the beach.'

Buster wagged his tail.

'I'll unpack later,' I called to Mum as I ran out the front door.

The waves pounded. The surf rolled in. Buster ran along the shoreline with me.

We hadn't gone very far, when we came to some very large rocks. They jutted out into the water.

Buster ran quickly over the rocks, ahead of me.

'Four legs sure would be good,' I said to myself, as I scrambled after him.

Safely over the rocks, I looked out to sea. I could see that a huge swell was building.

And in the next second, a gigantic wave washed right over us.

The wave swept us into the swirling water.

I tried to swim back towards the rocks. But the current was too strong.

The undertow was dragging me down and back out to sea. Buster was a few metres away. And he was struggling too.

I tried to remember everything I'd ever learned at swimming classes.

Keep calm. Don't panic.

But the water was cold. My arms and legs felt heavy, very heavy.

And I was swallowing mouthfuls of sea water.

It was then that I saw the white light. And I felt the sea mist closing around me, wrapping me in its icy fingers.

I was kind of spinning. And then it was as though I was being sucked down. Down into the watery depths of the ocean.

Chapter 2

Cootamara Island

I felt myself being lifted, lifted up out of the water by strong arms.

I was gasping. But I wasn't struggling anymore.

Somehow, I knew that whoever was holding me would take care of me.

I was lying on the beach. I could feel the sun warming my skin.

Buster was lying near me. He was dripping wet.

I reached across and touched him. I could feel the rise and fall of his chest. He was alive.

Then something moved beside me. I tried to sit up.

'I'd take it slowly,' a voice said.

My head was spinning. And for a minute I thought I
was going to vomit. I sat up slowly.

I found myself looking into the face of the oldest surf dude you could ever imagine.

His hair was sun-bleached and tied back in a ponytail. His face was tanned and lined. And his limbs were taut and strong.

His shorts were worn and torn. He smelt of salt and seaweed and the sea, like he was part of it.

24

'I'm Al.' He smiled as he took my hand.

'Hi, I'm Luke,' I replied.

'That was a close call,' he said. 'You'll need to sit and take it easy for a while.'

I nodded.

'Look out there,' he said, as he pointed into the wild waves.

I looked, but at first I could see nothing. Then I looked again. And far out beyond the reef, I could see figures on surfboards riding a wild surf.

25

I don't know too much about surfing. But I do know that these guys were doing some amazing stuff. They rode easily upon the crests of waves the size of two-storey buildings.

They rode upside down and inside the waves as the waves curled over them. And they ripped over the reef as if it wasn't there.

One guy was doing high aerials off the backwash.

And as they came closer, I could see the smiles on their faces, from the joy and the thrill of the challenge.

'Who are they?' I asked.

'They're the reef riders,' Al answered.

'But, but, those gigantic waves!' I said. 'I can't believe they can surf waves that high.'

'No problem,' said Al.

To me there was a problem. A huge one. No normal person could be riding those waves. There was just no way. So who were these guys?

I looked back at Al. He was watching the reef riders as if he really wanted to be out there with them. Perhaps he had been once. Or perhaps he would normally be out there. And I was the reason he wasn't.

'What is the name of this beach?' I asked.

I couldn't even see our beach house from here. And nothing seemed familiar.

Al looked at me then, with the bluest eyes I've ever seen.

'It's our paradise, Luke. We call it Cootamara Island.'

Chapter 3

The Wildest Wave

We watched the reef riders for a few minutes.

Then Al said, 'It's time you went back.'

I didn't want to leave. Not so soon.

'But how do we get back?' I asked.

'On that,' Al said.

He pointed to an old surfboard lying a few metres away. It was at least three metres long. And heavy. Not the light fibreglass type you see today.

'I'll take your dog first, if that's okay?' said Al.

'Sure,' I said.

I watched with awe. Al paddled into the surf with
Buster sitting happily on the front of the board.
Seconds later they had disappeared out over the reef.

Only minutes seemed to pass before Al returned.

'Your turn,' he said.

Like Buster, I knelt on the front of Al's board. We flew effortlessly over the reef, before we caught the wildest wave. I clung to the board with all my might.

It seemed only seconds later that we were back at Eastern Beach.

The old board slid right up onto the sand.

Buster was waiting for me, shaking himself dry.

I stood up and looked at Al. He was smiling.

'Thanks for saving us,' I said.

'No problem,' said Al. 'Pleased I could help.'

Al grabbed his board. And in a split second
he had gone.

Chapter 4

Goodbye

I looked further out to sea.

And right on the edge of the horizon, I thought I
could just see the reef riders surfing the waves.

I blinked. They were gone.

I reached down and ruffled Buster's hair. 'Come on fella. Let's go home.'

Buster gave a loud bark.

I didn't tell Mum what had happened on the beach. If I had, I knew she'd never let me down there again.

The following day I noticed some old photographs that were pinned on the walls of the surf club.
One of the photos was of a group of guys in daggy bathers. They were holding on to big, heavy-looking surfboards. Just like Al's.

Next to the photo was a faded newspaper clipping.

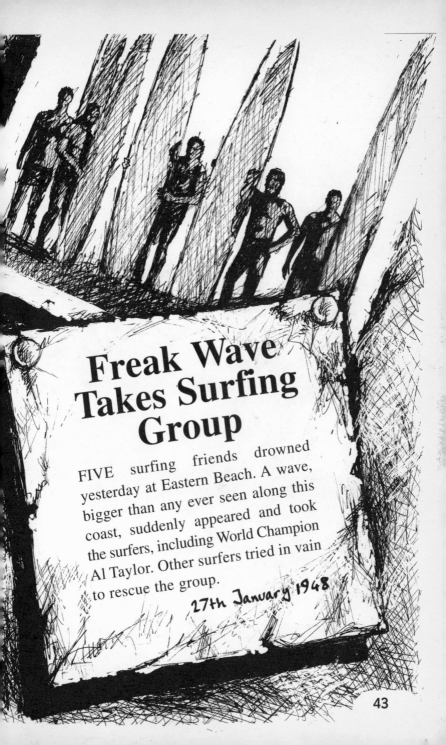

Freak Wave Takes Surfing Group

FIVE surfing friends drowned yesterday at Eastern Beach. A wave, bigger than any ever seen along this coast, suddenly appeared and took the surfers, including World Champion Al Taylor. Other surfers tried in vain to rescue the group.

27th January 1948

43

My eyes fell to the bottom of the page. The clipping was dated 27 January, 1948.

I looked more closely at the photo. The surfer, third on the left, was Al. I'd know his face anywhere.

I smiled at the photograph. Thanks Al.

Corinne Fenton

When I was a kid I loved to watch the surfers ride the waves at the beach near our holiday house.

I loved the freedom of the surf beach.

And I loved the feel of the wind on my face.

I used to walk at the water's edge on the golden sand and pick up the most amazing shells. And I would sit and just watch those surfers for hours, trying to catch the perfect wave. Perhaps one of them was Al?

Mark playing guitar, 1968

Illustrator Snapshot

Mark Wilson

I was thirteen years old in 1963 when I heard *The Beatles* on the radio. From that moment, I decided I was going to be a rock 'n' roll star. My older brother gave me his drum kit. I drove my family and neighbours crazy, practising every day after school.

My other love was drawing. We didn't have a TV until the late 60s. My brother and I spent each night drawing ships and planes on huge sheets of paper.

My dreams were to play rock 'n' roll and to be an artist. I'm still doing both today. So don't let go of your dreams, they *do* come true.

Read **These**